C000059347

SNORING

The Fun
The Facts
The Remedies
The Solutions

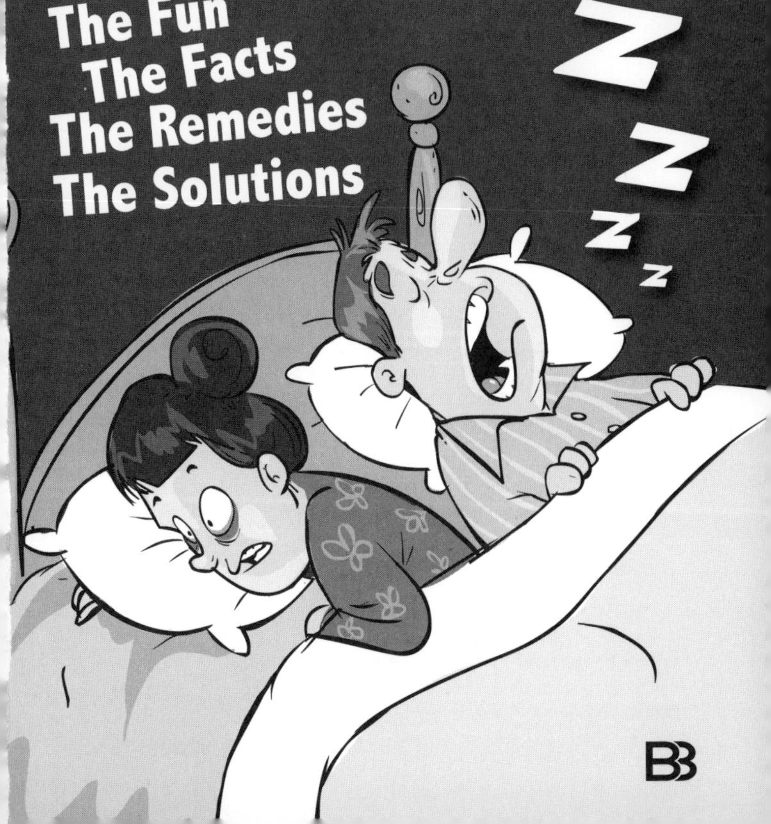

books by
BOXER

www.booksbyboxer.com

Published in the UK by
Books By Boxer, Leeds, LS13 4BS
© Books By Boxer 2016
All Rights Reserved

ISBN: 9781909732384

The Problem

It is estimated that a third of the population may indulge in audible snoring. Snoring can create over 90 decibels, equivalent to a lawnmower or a chainsaw (where ear muffs are considered a necessity).

RAARRRR!!!

RAARRRR!!!

It is said we all snore sometimes. Even those who consider themselves 'non snorers', under close observation, at certain times during sleep, will usually make sounds of snoring, however imperceptive.

These soft murmurings are generally the natural mechanisms of the patterns of sleep. Louder snoring though can be annoying, relationship threatening and, in some extreme cases, it can be downright dangerous.

Dangerous if you have 'sleep apnoea', a condition where breathing is paused during snoring but also if your partner decides to attack you with murderous intent (there are several recorded cases of the defence of homicide due to diminished responsibility as a result of being driven mad by their partner's snoring).

There are many reasons why people snore. Changes in the body can cause an onset of louder snoring. Some women begin to snore during pregnancy, particularly at the later stages. Similarly, the onset of menopause can have the same effect.

However, men snore more frequently and more loudly than women. This is partly due to the difference in anatomy but also, the relative difference in lifestyles. Male preferences for abundant quantities of beer before bedtime may result in the wrong kind of 'sound' sleep.

Illnesses, such as colds and flu that affect the throat can cause snoring and the more obese a person becomes, the more they are likely to snore. Some medications may increase the incidence of snoring and an over indulgence in alcohol can certainly be a factor.

THE CAUSE

Snoring can occur when we are in a very relaxed sleeping state, or when there is poor muscle tone in the throat and tongue. Alcohol, certain drugs and too much fat tissue can cause it. When muscles are too relaxed, the tongue falls backwards into the airway and/or the throat muscles draw in from the sides, narrowing the passages. When air tries to pass through these obstacles, the snoring sound results.

Snoring is the vibration of respiratory structures and the resulting sound due to obstructed air movement during breathing while sleeping. In some cases, the sound may be soft, but in other

cases, it can be loud and unpleasant. Snoring during sleep may be a sign, or first alarm, of obstructive sleep apnoea (OSA). Researchers say that snoring is a factor of sleep deprivation.

THE RESULT

Even setting aside the noise pollution, sleep deprivation for the snorer, and for those around that person, can cause daytime drowsiness, loss of mental function, irritability and loss of libido. Obstructive sleep apnoea (OSA), apnoea literally meaning loss of breath, is where the sufferer stops breathing regularly for periods of between 20 and 40 seconds. Those with OSA have a 30% increased chance of a heart attack. Although the subject of snoring is treated generally in a light hearted way, it can be the cause of severe relationship break down, being ostracised from certain activities and be the cause of anger, and even violence.

THE DIAGNOSIS

Snorers fall into categories of 'Mouth Breathers', 'Nasal Breathers' and 'Tongue Based Snorers' and this needs to be established before some gadgets are used, ideally by seeking medical advice. Try to pinpoint why you snore. Working out what's making you snore means you can treat it with much more success than if you're trying remedies in the dark (even though you might well try them in the dark!)

You should also examine your lifestyle and diet. Are you overweight? Do you drink alcohol before bedtime? Is the structure of your mouth the culprit? Have your doctor check it out. The way you sleep when snoring may also indicate the problem.

It has been speculated that-

Closed Mouth Snoring
If your mouth stays shut but you snore on, it may indicate a problem with your tongue/nasal passageways.

Snoring With Your Mouth Wide Open
The tissues in your throat may be more likely to be causing you to snore with

your mouth open. If your throat is partially obstructed, you're apt to try to force in more air when you sleep, aka... snoring.

Snoring On Your Back

Often when on our back we breathe through our mouths, which can exacerbate snoring.

Snoring Regardless Of Position

Possibly the sign of a more serious problem, such as sleep apnoea. See your doctor if your snoring is loud enough to keep your partner awake or, if you wake yourself up.

Catathrenia

This is a kind of snoring in reverse. It manifests itself by occasional groaning in sleep made on the out breath, (unlike snoring which is generated on the in breath). It is often similar to sexual noises and can be quite loud. As an explanation to the neighbours, a doctor's note might be necessary.

Tongue Based Snoring

If you are able to make a snoring noise with your mouth open and closed, try sticking your tongue out as far as you can and then grip it with your teeth. Try to make a snoring noise. If it is reduced, you are probably a tongue based snorer.

This means your tongue is vibrating, and is likely the cause of the problem.

THE CURES

There are many gadgets and remedies on the market that claim to cure the problem of snoring, the success or otherwise being subjective to the individual who tries them. There are also natural remedies, ancient remedies, bizarre remedies, witchcraft spells and D.I.Y contraptions, exercises and training. Those whose life is affected by loud and unpleasant snoring will often try one or more of these remedies.

PREVENTION

In The Bedroom - Sleeping position

You are more prone to snore if you sleep on your back. Sleeping face down reduces the incidence of snoring but is uncomfortable for most people. The most common disincentive snorers to sleep on their backs is a dig in the ribs from their long suffering sleeping partner. Make it difficult for snorers to sleep on their back by sewing a sock with a tennis ball inside to the outside middle of the back of a pyjama top or place the same ball in the front pocket of a shirt and wear it backwards. A small cudgel under the pillow, however tempting, is not recommended.

Bed Alignment

Elevating the bed so that the head is raised can reduce snoring by easing tension in the throat and relieving some pressure. You can raise the head of your bed about 4 inches or so, which may help keep your tongue from falling back and blocking your throat, and may help open up your airways a little bit.

You will need:
Sturdy blocks of wood. (about 1-2 inches thick, or books of a similar width)

Directions:
If you don't have wood lying around that you can use, you can pick up some

scrap timber easily at some hardware stores. It should be flat, square, and about 1-2 inches thick. Make sure it is wide enough to thoroughly cover the base of the foot of the bed you will be resting on it. Add these blocks 1 by 1 until you've reached about 4 inches. If you'd prefer to use books instead, just pop some under the feet at the head of the bed. In both cases, but particularly with books because of their uneven size, make sure the bed is steady and doesn't wobble, otherwise a night of passion might rock the bed off its perch.

Humidify

If you sleep in a room with dry air, it's possible that its causing you to snore. Dry air dries out our throat and nasal membranes and contributes to congestion. This restricts air movement, and will set your tissues vibrating. If this is your particular problem there are two ways to going about treating your snoring, buy a humidifier, or move to an exotic tropical location.

Dust mites

Change bed covers and pillow covers regularly to prevent this problem. Also wash the covers using an anti-allergen washing powder.

Replace Your Pillows

Your pillows may contain bacteria or allergens that may irritate your throat. You can buy anti-allergenic pillows that reduce the incidence of this. Also, higher pillows can give an improved head/torso angle that can improve breathing efficiency.

Keep Hydrated

Dehydration leading to a dry throat can increase the incidence of snoring. Half a glass of warm water before you go to bed is very beneficial. Always keep a glass of water handy in the bedroom for the middle of the night.

Lifestyle

Avoid or reduce alcohol intake. Booze might seem a good idea to get a good nights sleep, but alcohol can cause muscles in the throat to relax more than normal during sleep, resulting in reduced air flow, causing snoring.

Being Overweight

This increases the risk of snoring especially if the extra weight is around the neck area. Some people notice that they tend to snore as they grow older and this is generally due to being more overweight with age. Often, losing weight is a simple answer to the snoring problem but that can be easier said than done.

Being Overtired

If you are overtired when you go to bed you may sleep too deeply, not making the regular changes in position necessary for a good night sleep. This can render you more likely to snore.

Eat A Healthy Diet

A healthy, well balanced diet can help to alleviate the snoring problem. Certain foods are reputed to be specifically good for this, soy milk, tea, honey, turmeric, fish, onions are the most noted. So if you make yourself a meal of fish with turmeric and onions, washed down with soy milk tea with a spoon of honey then this should give you a good, quiet night sleep!

Don't Eat, Or Drink Alcohol Before Bed

If you leave a few hours between eating or drinking before you go to sleep you will have a more restful night.

Keep up on the house cleaning

As much as we (don't?) love cleaning, keeping your living quarters spick and span can pay off in the end. Allergens like pollen, dust, animal fluff, and other unseen irritants can cause congestion and irritate your airways, both of which can contribute to snoring. So roll up your sleeves and clean the place down! Also make sure you're changing your air filters on vacuum cleaners on a regular basis.

Remove allergy triggers

Fibres from plush toys and cushions may cause irritation that you are maybe not aware of. Keeping pets out of the sleeping area may be a good idea for the same reason if this type of allergy is suspected.

Avoid Milk Product

Cheese may actually give you nightmares -avoiding milk and milk products before going to bed can be beneficial to the snorer. Milk products increase the production of mucus.

Pets

Some allergies from pets can manifest themselves as triggers to the onset of snoring.

Smoking

As you might expect, smoking is bad for everything including snoring. Smoking aggravates the throat tissues causing them to vibrate more.

MEDICAL, NATURAL AND ALTERATIVE REMEDIES

Blocked Nasal Passages

There are certain scents that can increase your breathing ability. If you've ever had a cold or bad nasal congestion, you've probably taken medication that has menthol in it.

Menthol can naturally open the airways in the nose and throat. Menthol comes in essential oil form, and can be used every night. Make a 50/50 mixture of the essential oil and water and spritz it around the head of the bed every night before going to sleep.

Other essential oils you can use to open your airways are eucalyptus and mint.

Using Nasal Strips

According to the manufacturers, they open the nose, up to 38% more, allowing you to breathe more easily.

A Spoonful Of Honey Before You Go To Bed

Honey is well known as a salve for the throat that helps to lubricate and relax the muscles that exacerbate snoring.
Bees don't snore...
but they do buzz a bit!

Acupuncture

If other remedies are not having an effect then a course of acupuncture may help to relieve the problem. There is evidence that this alternative treatment often has a successful result.

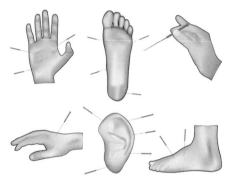

Hypnosis

Similarly, you may want to try hypnosis in searching for a cure for this problem. There are many who claim to have been cured by this method.

Natural Remedies

These are worth trying and some stores will give you good advice on the best ones to take.

(1) Make a SPRAY from ¼ tsp salt, ½ cup of boiling water. Cool and then put 2-3 squirts into each nostril. (Keep only for 5 days)

(2) To create an anti-inflammatory, use a few drops of mint oil in a small amount of boiling water. Inhale the steam.

(3) Green tea contains theanine, which helps promote sleep. Drink decaf green tea if you're drinking it just before bed.

(4) Take ½ tsp of extra virgin olive oil before retiring.

(5) Take a small handful of sage leaves, ½ tsp of apple vinegar and mix into 1 cup of boiling water.
Allow to cool then gargle with it.

(6) Take 4-6 drops of thyme oil and mix with 4-6 drops of vegetable oil.
Apply this to the feet.
This, apparently, has a beneficial effect for snorers.
(May be even more effective if you and your bed sharer top & tail!)

(7) Take 2-4 drops of Eucalyptus oil and mix in a largish bowl of boiling water. Put a towel over your head and the bowl and inhale the contents.

(8) Make a ginger tea from sliced ginger, honey and boiling water. Sip at bedtime.

Flatulence

Snoring and farting seem to be interconnected, particularly in men, possibly due to dietary issues (or beer!). The Chinese cure for flatulence, mix half a teaspoon of ginger powder in a small glass of warm water, is also reputed to reduce snoring.

Cannabis

Some swear by this remedy but obviously, as it's an illegal drug in most places, therefore cannot be recommended here.

Tryptophan

Tryptophan is one of the essential amino acids. The body uses tryptophan to help produce serotonin. Serotonin is thought to produce healthy sleep and a stable mood which are conditions conducive to reducing snoring. The main foods containing tryptophan are: cheese, chicken, eggs, fish, milk, nuts, peanut butter, peanuts, pumpkin seeds, sesame seeds, soy, tofu, turkey, raw soya beans and bananas.

Menopause

Keep the menopause at bay!
The onset of menopause can produce snoring where none occurred before.

EXERCISES AND PROCEDURES

Mouth And Jaw Exercises

Some members of the medical profession believe the condition of the mouth, jaw and throat can be responsible for excessive snoring.

Certain exercises can improve this condition. Rarely has chewing gum been seen as a health positive but the action of chewing strengthens the jaw muscles.

Other exercises include:
• Pushing out the lower jaw further than the upper jaw as a regular repetitive exercise.

• Opening the jaws wide and relaxing.

• The facial formations of 'blowing a kiss'.

• Smiling a lot.

- Sipping rather than drinking tea, coffee, water or soft drinks.

- Stretch the lips and push the tongue out as far as possible (not in polite company).

- Say 'aahh' several times, push the tongue against the lower teeth.

- Work the swallowing muscles.

- Work your jaw left and right gently.

All these exercises should be done carefully and without excess strain to avoid possible injuries.

Gargling

There appears to be several options of what substances one may use to gargle with, to soothe and relax the throat before retiring.

Water infused with garlic appears to be at the top of the list, (which may not be great as a precursor to a night of passion). Fish oil could probably have a similar effect on your oral hygiene attractiveness, though the Chinese consider it an aphrodisiac. The author's favourite gargle, as recommended by some texts on the subject of snoring, is whisky (or whiskey, if you prefer the Irish version).

Steam breathing

Spend 10 minutes under a blanket as you inhale steam. It's cheap and effective. This should clear your nasal congestion and reduce or eliminate snoring when you go to bed. However, you have to be pretty desperate to do this every night.

Yoga

Asana practices such as yogic breathing and inverted or backward exercises can reduce snoring problems.

Pranayama is a type of yoga exercise dedicated to learning how to control your breathing.

You master taking deep, slow, breaths and get the most out of the oxygen around you. It aids in the delivery of blood to the brain and overall increases circulation. It is also an incredible technique for relaxation.

Pranayama has been used to relieve various sleep disorders, including sleep apnoea.

Check out some classes or find a good book and practice at home, to possibly reduce or eliminate your snoring. You will feel rested, rejuvenated, and energized as a result.

Nasal Irrigation

A nasal irrigation method involves flushing out your nasal passages. You do this by using a nasal syringe, and warm salt water. By flushing out your nasal passages with a warm, saltwater solution, you get rid of dust and debris that block the sinuses. This is a great method to use if you have a bad head cold or if you suffer from sinus problems. When you have no clogs in your nasal passages, you have an easier time breathing at night.

Abdominal Breathing

This is a deeper form of breathing where you use your diaphragm more than the rise and fall of the chest wall to fill your lungs more fully. You initiate inward breathing by allowing your diaphragm to expand fully before using the chest muscles to draw in more air. This should be built up slowly as the extra oxygen created by the uninitiated can make you light headed. However, it is very good for the system and can reduce snoring. 'Abs' exercises involving the solar plexus (such as sit-ups) can be helpful in this.

Flabby palate

This is a common snoring problem, particularly in old age. This can be improved by exercising the soft palate in the roof of the mouth. The exercise to do is difficult to describe, nearest being: with the top of your tongue held against the palate, suck hard on the back of your tongue.

Nasal Septum Deviation

This is a condition in which the nasal septum, the bone and cartilage that divide the nasal cavity of the nose in half, is significantly off centre, or crooked, making breathing difficult. This also is a cause of snoring. 80% of people have some kind of misalignment in their nasal breathing passages that are, normally, not a problem. Surgery may be necessary to cure the most extreme imbalances.

Age – Be Younger!

Unfortunately, the throat narrows with age and there is not much that can be done about this. Surgery is possible in the case of extreme problems arising from this condition.

Men

Men simply have narrower air passages than women and this increases the likelihood of snoring. Some women say they are allergic to men... could this also be a cause?

STOP SNORING – THE FUN WAY!

Singing

The condition of the throat of a professional singer is vital to their performance and many hours of practice are required to keep the necessary muscles in top physical shape. Singing has been proven to reduce the levels of snoring in individuals who have a high incidence of this problem. Therefore, keep singing in the shower (or elsewhere) for at least 15-20 minutes per day. This method has the added bonus that it can make the original snoring not sound as bad in comparison to the singing!

Playing A Wind Instrument

Playing a wind instrument such as the trumpet, trombone, bagpipes, saxophone or even the recorder will improve your lung capacity and strengthen the muscles of the mouth and throat. It has been said that playing the Didgeridoo is a fairly serious remedy for the snorer. Your partner, however, may prefer the snoring to the musical discord that you will most likely produce as you learn to play your new instrument.

Booze and Sex

Here is a tongue in cheek remedy for the imaginative snorer and 'bed sharer'. Both parties get dead drunk and have noisy, gratuitous sex. Both sleep so well that each cannot hear the other's snoring. Better than a night of 'nasal spray' or 'face mask', methinks!

Vodka

According to many 'babushkas' in Russia, vodka cures colds, sore throats and also cures snoring, by relaxing the soft tissues in the throat and nose. Some of this may be true but it is most likely that the 'bed sharer', after drinking a decent amount of vodka, will get an uninterrupted night's sleep.

MORE EXTREME MEASURES

Strychnine
According to the archives, this works very well. However, it is highly poisonous, so NOT recommended here (however, if anyone is prepared to try it we will be interested in a product review!).

Electric Shock Treatment
Apparently there is a device on the market that is worn on the wrist, is sound activated, and delivers a mild electric shock when it detects snoring. Apparently it is quite effective and is supposed to be 100% effective if connected to one's private parts, but

the subsequent noise created by such an intimate shock may be much more disturbing through the night than any snoring.

Tape
An extreme form of SAA (snore avoidance activity) is taping one's mouth shut, which may have dangerous consequences. NOT recommended.

Strap Around The Chest

A bizarre remedy from Eastern Europe to reduce the incidence of snoring is to fix a wide belt around your chest.

This is supposed to reduce the large breath intake that often accompanies snoring.

Fixing the belt too tight would cause asphyxiation, heart failure and death.

Not to be recommended.

DEVICES

CPAC Machines

CPAC machines are ventilation machines that forces air into the respiratory system via a mask or mouth piece which appears to be 100% effective for sleep apnoea.

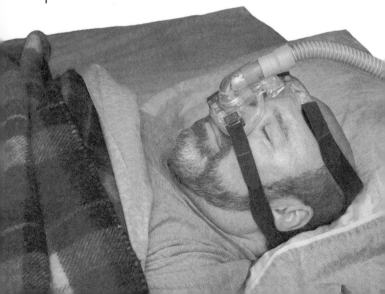

Jaw Supporter

This is a kind of elasticated soft strap that goes under the chin and over the head, with holes for the ears to pop through. This keeps the jaw in an upright forward position, forcing the mouth to be closed. This has the effect of disallowing snoring through the mouth. Can be uncomfortable until one gets used to it... if ever.

Snore Ring

When worn, the snore ring applies acupuncture pressure to nerve points in the little finger. This in turn is intended to relax certain muscles in the throat and so reduce the likelihood of snoring.

Nasal Strips

Nasal strips are Band Aid type plasters, but with a flat plastic interior which when adhered to the bridge of the nose, pulls open the nostrils, allowing a clearer air passage.

These are often used by athletes and sometimes by racehorses and are generally regarded as good for some types of snoring. These are best suited as a remedy if snoring occurs in the nose.

You can actually make these yourself, though they are generally not expensive to buy.
Cut a piece of soft but springy flat

plastic (as the type from the lid of a Pringles pack). Fix this inside an adhesive bandage (band aid type) or use Sellotape, and give it a try.

Nasal Sprays

Nasal sprays are used as a decongestant and can be useful in the case of nasal snoring. Many are anti-inflammatory and some act as desensitizers.

Care should be taken when choosing a nasal spray, as there can be some side effects such as, chronic rebound congestion, the swelling of the nasal passage which has the opposite to the desired affect!

Nasal Cones

These are like 2 connected little plastic baskets that push up you nose to open the airways.

There are problems here of getting a good fit!

You can't exactly go to the pharmacist store and keep on trying different ones until you find the right size, and, as they are quite tiny, there is a small chance you might swallow them in the night.

Nasal Drops

These work in a similar way to the nasal sprays but using a different method of application. Probably as effective as many are a simple saline (saltwater) solution that you can prepare yourself.

Ear Plugs

These may be an essential night time accessory for the 'bed sharer'. They can be useful for the snorer too as loud snorers can wake themselves up.

Headphones

Another important accessory, in the attempt of the 'bed sharer' to drown out the noise.

Bedside Fan

It is said that cool air circulating near the snorer can reduce the level and incidence of snoring. Hopefully, the drone of the fan might mask some of the noise as well.

Snoring Mouthpieces

There are possibly hundreds of different mouthpieces that claim to stop snoring. Some work on the technique of restraining the tongue, TSD (Tongue Stabilising Devices) while the others are just plain MAD (Mandibular Advancement Devices). MAD devices keep the lower jaw forward to lessen the risk of snoring. Suitability, as to discomfort or effectiveness, can only be ascertained through trials by the user and, given the number of such devices on the market, this could be a long and expensive task.

Sleep Disorders Centre & Sleep Labs

In persistent cases you may be referred to a specialist clinic that are used to monitor sleep patterns and will give a diagnosis of your condition followed by recommendations. In suspected cases of severe sleep apnoea, this could be a vital resource.

Robotic Bear

A research group from Waseda University in Tokyo has come up with a robotic bear that flips over people's heads in their sleep to open their airways.

The bear works as a pillow with a built-in microphone. If it detects loud snoring, a paw reaches up to turn the snorer's head sideways

As soon as Jukusui-kun (the bear) detects a loud snore, his paw reaches up (gently, at least in the brief video demo on display), and pushes the sleeper's head to one side.

The motion should push sufferers of sleep apnoea into a position where they no longer snore.

SOME SNORING FACTS, ANECDOTES AND REFERENCES

Animals

Snoring in dogs is often due to obesity. Black bears snore loudly during hibernation. They also fart quite a lot during this period.

Charles Dickens
Charles Dickens referred to Fat Joe's snoring in the Pickwick Papers.

William Makepeace Thackeray
"This gentle, unromantic music of the nose".

Places You Shouldn't Snore

In a youth hostel, on a train, in a restaurant, in a school class, on the bus, on a first date, at work, on an airplane, in the theatre, when your mother in law shows you her holiday snaps.

★ Why does the one who snores, ★
always go to sleep first.

Middle Age
40% of middle aged men snore and at least 28% of middle aged women.

Americans
90 million Americans snore. This puts them fairly high on the snoring leader board per head of population.

Scandinavians
Scandanavians snore the least per head of population.

Noise
The average decibel level of a snore is 38 decibels.

Laugh

"Laugh and the world laughs with you... snore and you sleep alone".

Anthony Burgess

Children

5.6% of children snore (Vancouver Sleep and Breathing Center).

Dogs And Cats

Overweight animals tend to snore. It's estimated that 21% of dogs snore and only 7% of cats.

FAT DOG ↘

FAT CAT ←

Mark Twain

"A use has been found for everything, - except snoring".

Dreaming

It is said that if you are snoring, you can't be dreaming, though nobody has really found out.

Snoring Is Normal

Forty-five percent of normal adults snore occasionally, and 25 percent snore habitually. Twice as many men snore as women.

Record Breaker!

The loudest snore (recorded in the Guinness Book of Records) was 92 decibels, by Melvin Switzer. That's about the same as a pneumatic drill or a food blender.

Devices

The UK patent office lists over 2000 devices to prevent or treat snoring! Yet in many cases, simply turning onto your side may be all that is needed.

Bizarre Laws

By Law Snoring in Massachusetts is prohibited unless all bedroom windows are closed and securely locked.

CELEBRITY SNORING

Tom Cruise

Tom created a 'snoratorium', a room he could snore without his (ex) wife Katie Holmes being disturbed.

Judge Judy

The judge has a snoring room because when she's in full 'session' her family holds her in contempt.

Prince Harry

Prince William said of his brother, "He snores a lot and keeps me up all night long".

Teddy Roosevelt

The former president of the United States had to be moved to another floor in a hospital where he was staying so other patients could get 'a good nights sleep'. He was considerably overweight.

Marilyn Manson

"Marilyn's soft, rhythmic, soothing snoring lulls me to sleep" said girlfriend, Evan Rachel Wood.

Franklin Delano Roosevelt

Also a former US president. He had a bad snoring affliction, possibly due to his heavy smoking.

Lionel Messi

This international football star apparently 'snores a lot'. This was the verdict of his room mate, Juan Sebastian Veron, at the 2010 world cup.

Elizabeth Taylor

According to the indiscretions of her sleeping partners, Lzzzzz, (as she was sometimes referred to) was a loud snorer. She also had a series of unlucky marriages and possibly the two were linked.

Winston Churchill

It is rumoured that the Great British Bulldog actually sounded like one when he snored and roared the night away. The former prime minister's fondness for cigars and late

night alcohol probably accounted for some of it.

Billy Connolly

Billy has tried several snoring remedies. Perhaps it wasn't his 'wee little dog' that could cause a D-I-V-O-R-C-E !

Queen Victoria

The queen in later life acquired a certain amount of excess weight that probably accounted for her nocturnal noise levels. Presumably her nearest and dearest were 'not amused'.

Napoleon

Among his many health problems, including bad haemorrhoids, Boney also had problems between the sheets. His sexual prowess was without question, according to reports by Josephine and others. But, particularly as he got older and put on a bit of midriff, he was a high decibel snorer. Perhaps his chat up line of, 'I will keep you up all night, ma cherie', meant something entirely different.

Rihanna

The Barbadian singing superstar snored so loudly during an American Airlines flight from Miami that she issued a public apology to everyone on the flight. No one said, 'I love the way you lie'.

Matt Damon

The Bourne Identity star admitted that he had hypnosis to try and get his snoring under control. Ex-girlfriends, Winona Ryder and Minnie Driver complained about the noise but he didn't seek help until his own sleep began to be disturbed.

Ethan Hawke

Uma Thurman got divorced from Ethan and snoring was not cited as the cause of the breakdown. However, Uma discreetly told the world that, with Ethan, it was like sleeping with a herd of bellowing elephants.

David Arquette

Courteney Cox of Friends fame, the ex-wife of actor David, said that the walls shook with his reverberating snores.

Ashley Tisdale

The Disney star used to snore so loudly that she would wake herself up. She then had an operation for her deviated septum, which cured the problem.

Guy Ritchie

The Yorkshire born international film director's (ex) missus, Madonna, insisted on separate bedrooms because of Guy's persistent snoring. The 'ale-loving' (Taylor's 'Landlord' Bitter) film director said, "She doesn't like it at all. She boots me out of bed when it goes off the scale".

Prince Charles

The Prince of Wales was teased for snoring when he attended Gordonstoun school. Other boys at the school even recorded him to show how loud it was.

JUNGLE WARFARE

In jungle warfare, snoring would be particularly dangerous. Modern day soldiers still use tricks taught at the British Jungle Warfare School in Johore Bahru, Malaysia. The most effective technique was to tuck a fold of poncho liner into your mouth and grip it with teeth. This still could allow nasal snoring but would prevent the loudest noises made by the throat and mouth.

An extract from the book, 'INSIDE NEW ZEALAND'S SAS, Ron Crosby (NZSAS-first fifty years)
Snoring could also compromise your life. After a particularly noisy night, one soldier was instructed that if he snored

the next night the patrol would move about 250 metres away from him for its safety and leave him on his own.
They did not hear him snore again.

MORE FACTS

- There are 15 million snorers in the UK. 10.5 million men and 4.5 million women.

- The 3 main reasons for snoring are: being overweight, smoking and drinking alcohol.

- Snoring sound is air turbulance vibrating the structures in the upper airway.

- The louder you snore, the more likely you are to be overweight.

- Snoring sounds range from 50dB to 100dB - the equivalent to a pneumatic drill.

- Snorers are 3 times more likely to suffer adverse health conditions than non-snorers.

- Snoring can be hereditary - nearly 70% of snorers have a familial link.

- 'Bed sharers' of snorers report they have just 3-5 hours sleep per night.

- 'Bed sharers' of snorers visit their GP more frequently than 'bed sharers' of non-snorers.

- Snorers and their 'bed sharers' are more likely to be hard of hearing than non-snorers and their sharers.

- Over one third of couples report disharmony within the relationship due to snoring.

- Sleep quality rather than quantity is more of an issue. Poor sleep quality exacerbates poor health.

- Sleep loss affects newly learned skills more than well-known skills.

- More than 1,000 studies of sleep deprivation have been published during the past 100 years.

- 'Bed sharers' of snorers physical and mental health improves significantly once the snorer has been treated successfully.

- Despite evidence to the contrary, 'bed sharers' report better sleep quality when sleeping with their snoring partner than when they sleep alone.

- In 1910 we were sleeping for approximately 9 hours per night. In 2009 we sleep for around 6-7 hours.

- More than 50% of patients with Obstructive Sleep Apnoea (OSA) have high blood pressure whereas only 25% of patients with high blood pressure have OSA.

- Regular snorers are 5 times more likely to develop hypertension, heart disease, stroke, Type 2 diabetes and high cholesterol than occasional snorers.

'Snore' once meant the same as 'snort' and was applied to animals. Shakespeare was the first to use the verb for human snoring.

"Thou do'st snore distinctly, There's meaning in thy snores" (The Tempest).

In a divorce case in Iran in 1997, a woman admitted drugging her husband early in the marriage so that he would not hear her snoring.

"There ain't no way to find out why a snorer can't hear himself snore."
(Mark Twain from Tom Sawyer)

SNORING JOKES

★ Why don't bananas snore?

★ Because they don't want to wake up the rest of the bunch.

Use the 'snore stopper' pillow method.
1. Hold pillow over snorer's mouh.
2. Wait until snoring / breathing stops.
3. Delete this message.

I got a special snorer's mask because my snoring drives my partner crazy. It works a treat. I put it over my partners face and now I can't hear her complaining.

My new hot date promised me there would be no sleeping if he took me to bed. He was right... he snored all night.

I have to get a cure for this snoring, - otherwise I'll lose my job.

My wife snores, but only when we make love.

My wife tells me that I snore a lot. So I stayed up last night to see if I could hear myself, and.... nothing.

I think my new girlfriend really loves me very much. She lies awake all night listening to my snoring.

She told him that his snoring could wake the dead, so he stopped.
He got scared that he might wake his mother-in-law.

My wife's idea of getting some earplugs was brilliant.
Now I can't hear her complaining about my snoring.

★ Which dinosaur wakes up all the others?

★ The Bronte-snore-us.

I keep waking myself in the night with my snoring. I should be fine tonight though, I'm going to sleep in the spare room.

Last night, he took his snoring to new highs. It was heard three flights up.

When he said he was a sound sleeper, I didn't realize he would make a racket all night with his snoring.

My wife woke me up with her snoring last night.
I grabbed the steering wheel just in time.

My boyfriend's snoring is really bad. He's had his nose broken a few times.
It still didn't stop him.

I envy people who sleep next to someone who snore... because I lie awake all night next to someone who snores!

THE CONCLUSION

Snoring can be life threatening, annoying, soothing, irritating, to the point being cited as a reason for homicide, funny or tragic.

It is one of life's little problems that must be suffered or dealt with... for the sake of your health or the health of someone you sleep with.

As you will have learnt, you are not on your own, and there are cures available. Whether one learns to live with it or drown it out, make separate sleeping arrangements or sleep using one of the various gadgets on the market, use herbal remedies or learn to play the didgeridoo, it could be a life changing experience when you able to cure the roar!